**7** How do liberals view the state?

..................................................................................................................

..................................................................................................................

..................................................................................................................

**8** Why is the relationship between liberals and the state complicated? **4 marks**

..................................................................................................................

..................................................................................................................

..................................................................................................................

..................................................................................................................

## Rationalism

The Enlightenment belief in rationalism shapes liberal thinking. Liberals believe that humans are guided by reason and logic rather than emotion and instinct. People are capable of making their own moral choices and decisions about their best interests, rather than needing external guidance. Reason, specifically logic, is the only source of knowledge. This acceptance of rationalism has implications for society, as the consequences of rationalism are individual freedom and democratic consent being given to representatives to safeguard this freedom. The state is rejected as an organism; it exists only as a contract between individuals. In dealing with conflict, reason, not force, should be used to resolve any issues.

**9** How does the liberal belief in rationalism link to views on human nature? **2 marks**

..................................................................................................................

..................................................................................................................

### John Locke (1632–1704)

| Ideas | Statements |
|---|---|
| • Father of classical liberalism.<br>• Natural rights of man: individuals should make their own decisions about where and how they live.<br>• Social contract: government by the consent of the governed, who give up some personal freedoms in return for personal security. | • 'Every man has a property in his own person. This nobody has a right to, but himself.'<br>• 'Being all equal and independent, no one ought to harm another in his life, health, liberty, or possessions.' |

**10** What is Locke's *social contract*? **2 marks**

..................................................................................................................

..................................................................................................................

**11** How can Locke's arguments be linked to rationalism? **4 marks**

..................................................................................................................

..................................................................................................................

..................................................................................................................

..................................................................................................................

## Inequality and social justice

Liberals counter inequality in three forms. Foundational equality means that all individuals have equal moral worth, with an equal stake in society. Formal equality develops this further, giving all individuals legal and political equality. However, there are divisions within liberalism over how far equality should be interpreted. For classical liberals any extension beyond foundational and formal equality would effectively counter the freedom of individuals to succeed or fail. However, for modern liberals equality of opportunity is necessary to enable all to participate, and the state has a role to play in enabling this participation.

For modern liberals, the focus on social justice is a reaction to the capitalist idea that individuals deserve the fruits of their labour, which is considered unfair because natural inequalities within society mean that people do not necessarily receive what they are due. However, even modern liberals believe that economic inequalities should be removed rather than that all should have the opportunity to succeed economically.

**12** Explain the THREE forms of equality for liberals. *(6 marks)*

........................................................................................................

........................................................................................................

........................................................................................................

........................................................................................................

........................................................................................................

........................................................................................................

**13** How does social justice ensure a more equal society? *(2 marks)*

........................................................................................................

........................................................................................................

### Betty Friedan (1921–2006)

| Ideas | Statements |
|---|---|
| • Sought equal political and legal rights for women. <br> • Argued that marriage was an outdated institution which fettered women. | • 'Who knows what women can be when they are finally free to become themselves.' <br> • 'A girl should not expect special privileges because of her sex, but neither should she "adjust" to privilege and discrimination.' |

**14** How can Friedan's arguments be linked to liberal views of equality? *(4 marks)*

........................................................................................................

........................................................................................................

........................................................................................................

........................................................................................................

## Liberal democracy

Liberal democracy is seen by liberals as the form of government most likely to safeguard individualism. This is because it is based on the constitutional features of the rule of law and separation of powers, providing clear and enforceable rules which limit the power of government. Liberal democracy requires regular elections which are free, fair and based on universal adult suffrage. There is political equality among citizens, who are encouraged to participate actively in the democratic process. Although decision-making power is transferred to representatives, the electoral process means that the people have given their consent to government, ensuring its legitimacy.

Liberals may be wary of democracy as it has the potential to encroach upon individual freedoms and liberties. However, it is the form of government most likely to promote and safeguard civil rights and individual liberties.

**15** Outline THREE features of a liberal democracy.　　　3 marks

.......................................................................................................................

.......................................................................................................................

.......................................................................................................................

**16** How should liberal democracy be limited?　　　2 marks

.......................................................................................................................

.......................................................................................................................

**17** What are the positives of liberal democracy?　　　2 marks

.......................................................................................................................

.......................................................................................................................

### John Rawls (1921–2002)

| Ideas | Statements |
|---|---|
| • Modern liberalism: Rawls defended a more egalitarian liberalism.<br>• Argued for access to basic liberties which should be open to all — equality of opportunity. | • 'A just society is a society that if you knew everything about it, you'd be willing to enter it in a random place.'<br>• 'Liberal constitutional democracy is supposed to ensure that each citizen is free and equal and protected by basic rights and liberties.' |

**18** How can Rawls' arguments be linked to liberal democracy?　　　4 marks

.......................................................................................................................

.......................................................................................................................

.......................................................................................................................

.......................................................................................................................

.......................................................................................................................

.......................................................................................................................

# Differing views and tensions

## Classical liberalism

Classical liberalism has a complicated relationship with the state as it particularly emphasises strict limits to the size, role and nature of government. The relationship between the individual and the state is, as defined by Locke, one of a contract where governments represent individuals based upon the consent they have given. The state is regarded as, at best, a necessary nuisance with a role that should be confined to creating and enforcing the law: mainly to protect private property and to safeguard rights. These rights are based on the concept of foundational or formal equality, where all are born equal, with equal moral worth, and everyone should have the same formal status in society with same rights and entitlements: equality before the law.

**19** Define *foundational equality*.　　　2 marks

.......................................................................................................................

.......................................................................................................................

**20** What is the classical liberal view of the role of the state? 2 marks

.......................................................................................................................................................................
.......................................................................................................................................................................

For classical liberals all individuals are free and equal. Negative freedom, or freedom from, means freedom from any limits or restraints. Negative freedom advocates, for example, freedom of speech, freedom of association, freedom of property ownership and freedom from state interference. This is based on the idea that people are rational by nature: if they are left alone, they will tend to make the best decisions by themselves. The only role of the state for classical liberals within this concept of negative freedom is to keep the peace; the state would have no role in managing the economy. Otherwise the state is seen as a threat to freedom by classical liberals as it is the chief constraint on the freedom of individuals. In order to maximise negative freedom, the state must be minimal and not interfere in people's lives.

**21** Summarise *negative freedom*. 2 marks

.......................................................................................................................................................................
.......................................................................................................................................................................

**22** How do classical liberals justify the need for negative freedom? 4 marks

.......................................................................................................................................................................
.......................................................................................................................................................................
.......................................................................................................................................................................
.......................................................................................................................................................................
.......................................................................................................................................................................
.......................................................................................................................................................................

Classical liberals' conception of the market is derived from their views of the state. So laissez-faire economics and free trade are key features of a market that is characterised by a lack of state interference and control. This free market guarantees equality, as different talents should be rewarded differently and appropriately. Taxes should be limited or absent, as they punish the rich for their success and achievements, and detract from individual freedoms.

**23** Name TWO features of the classical liberal market. 2 marks

.......................................................................................................................................................................
.......................................................................................................................................................................

**24** What are the implications of the classical liberal view of the market? 2 marks

.......................................................................................................................................................................
.......................................................................................................................................................................
.......................................................................................................................................................................

## Modern liberalism

The poverty and often harsh nature of life in Victorian Britain led to the development of modern liberal views and values by the end of the nineteenth century. Politicians and theorists felt that there were weaknesses in classical liberal ideas and policies, which could not provide freedom for everyone, as shown by high levels of disease and squalor. In a similar fashion to the development of paternalism or 'one-nation' conservatism, modern liberal ideas took hold.

**25** **What circumstances were modern liberals reacting against?** `2 marks`

........................................................................................

........................................................................................

Equality of opportunity can only be achieved if there is a reduction in social inequality, which may lead to some equality of outcome. This would take place in conjunction with a more positive role for the state. The state would create the conditions in which people could excel, through education or improvements in health. This state would be an enabling state, one that would allow people to choose to progress, rather than one which intervened. The idea of choosing to advance can be described as developmental individualism.

**26** **Define *equality of opportunity*.** `2 marks`

........................................................................................

........................................................................................

**27** **What is the modern liberal view of the role of the state?** `2 marks`

........................................................................................

........................................................................................

It is important to recognise that although the two strands of liberalism view the role of the state differently, there are still overlaps. Both classical and modern liberals believe that freedom is the ultimate political goal, in whatever form it takes. Modern liberals believe in a positive freedom where the enabling state promotes equality of opportunity and creates the conditions for people to choose to progress, but they have not rejected negative freedom entirely. Their aim is to enable people to help themselves, thus the aim of both classical and modern liberals is to promote individual autonomy, or negative freedom. All liberal views on equality stem from a belief in individualism, and this is true for modern liberals whose belief in a relative form of social equality is still grounded in individualism.

**28** **Summarise *positive freedom*.** `2 marks`

........................................................................................

........................................................................................

**29** **What are the overlaps in classical and modern liberalism in terms of freedom?** `4 marks`

........................................................................................

........................................................................................

........................................................................................

........................................................................................

Qualified welfare allows positive freedom and equality of opportunity. A free market — one that is unregulated and free of state intervention, as favoured by classical liberals — creates inequalities in wealth and conditions similar to those in Victorian Britain. The state has a role to play, for modern liberals, in providing the welfare that enables individuals to help themselves. It is important to note that the increased role awarded to the state by modern liberals has the aim of providing welfare or regulating the economy and does NOT mean that modern liberals support constitutionalism or unlimited state power.

**30** **Why do modern liberals advocate qualified welfare?**　　2 marks

....................................................................................................................................
....................................................................................................................................

**31** **Are there limits to the role of the state for modern liberals?**　　2 marks

....................................................................................................................................
....................................................................................................................................

**32** **Did modern liberal ideas develop from classical liberal ideas and adapt to reflect the modern world, or are they entirely different from classical liberal ideas?**　　6 marks

....................................................................................................................................
....................................................................................................................................
....................................................................................................................................
....................................................................................................................................
....................................................................................................................................
....................................................................................................................................

## Summary table

**33** **Fill in the table.**

|  | Classical liberalism | Modern liberalism |
|---|---|---|
| Summarise views on the state. |  |  |
| Summarise views on freedom. |  |  |

|  | Classical liberalism | Modern liberalism |
|---|---|---|
| Thinkers |  |  |

**34** Fill in the table.

| What do classical and modern liberals agree on? | What do they disagree on? |
|---|---|
|  |  |

## Exam-style questions

**1** To what extent have modern liberals abandoned individualism and embraced collectivism? You must use appropriate thinkers you have studied to support your answer.

**35**  **24 marks**

*In the introduction, outline what is meant by the terms* individualism *and* collectivism. *Consider whether different strands of liberalism are more or less individualist than others.*

...............................................................................................................................

...............................................................................................................................

...............................................................................................................................

...............................................................................................................................

...............................................................................................................................

...............................................................................................................................

*Paragraph 1. Classical liberals favour individualism. Thinker: Locke.*

...............................................................................................................................

...............................................................................................................................

...............................................................................................................................

...............................................................................................................................

...............................................................................................................................

...............................................................................................................................

**Paragraph 2. Modern liberals have reduced the emphasis on individualism through their support for the enabling state and Keynesian economics. Thinker: Rawls.**

...........................................................................................................................................................
...........................................................................................................................................................
...........................................................................................................................................................
...........................................................................................................................................................
...........................................................................................................................................................
...........................................................................................................................................................
...........................................................................................................................................................
...........................................................................................................................................................

**Paragraph 3. What criticisms would classical liberals have of these views? Thinker: Mill.**

...........................................................................................................................................................
...........................................................................................................................................................
...........................................................................................................................................................
...........................................................................................................................................................
...........................................................................................................................................................
...........................................................................................................................................................
...........................................................................................................................................................
...........................................................................................................................................................
...........................................................................................................................................................

**Paragraph 4. Modern liberals are still rooted in individualism. State intervention is limited and focused on social and economic intervention only. Collectivism is only a means to an end. Thinkers: Wollstonecraft and Friedan.**

...........................................................................................................................................................
...........................................................................................................................................................
...........................................................................................................................................................
...........................................................................................................................................................
...........................................................................................................................................................
...........................................................................................................................................................
...........................................................................................................................................................
...........................................................................................................................................................

*Conclusion. Weigh up the evidence on both sides. Be clear that modern liberals are not aiming to create a nanny state but an environment in which individuals can flourish.*

.................................................................................................................................

.................................................................................................................................

.................................................................................................................................

.................................................................................................................................

.................................................................................................................................

.................................................................................................................................

.................................................................................................................................

.................................................................................................................................

.................................................................................................................................

.................................................................................................................................

.................................................................................................................................

.................................................................................................................................

.................................................................................................................................

.................................................................................................................................

.................................................................................................................................

.................................................................................................................................

**2** To what extent does modern liberalism depart from the ideas of classical liberalism? You must use appropriate thinkers you have studied to support your answer.

**35**  **24 marks**

*Make notes below and write your essay on a separate sheet of paper.*

.................................................................................................................................

.................................................................................................................................

.................................................................................................................................

.................................................................................................................................

.................................................................................................................................

.................................................................................................................................

.................................................................................................................................

.................................................................................................................................

.................................................................................................................................

.................................................................................................................................

.................................................................................................................................

.................................................................................................................................

.................................................................................................................................

.................................................................................................................................

.................................................................................................................................

.................................................................................................................................

# Topic 2

## Conservatism

## Core ideas and principles

Conservatism is a set of ideas and principles that focus upon the desire to maintain and conserve society as it is. Conservative thinkers are often suspicious of change, preferring to rely on ideas that are tried and tested (empiricism). This is based on a view of human nature that is shaped by mistrust and considers humans to be imperfect. As humans are seen as morally, psychologically and intellectually imperfect, conservatism has developed principles to counteract these tendencies.

### Pragmatism

For conservatives, pragmatism means having a flexible and practical response to circumstances rather than fixed ideological or doctrinal principles. This suggests a responsive rather than a fixed nature to conservatism, which differentiates it from other ideologies. Although conservatives appear to fear change and to prefer continuity, their pragmatic strand means that they regard some change or evolution as preferable to a dogmatic doctrinal response to changing circumstances. This reflects the conservative belief in 'reform that you may preserve' (Macaulay), demonstrating that pragmatic change can prevent more drastic upheaval. Examples of pragmatic responses to potential upheaval can be seen in the extension of the franchise, Disraeli's one-nation toryism and support for partial reform of the House of Lords. Ultimately, conservative pragmatism is founded upon enlightened self-interest.

---

**1** How have conservatives demonstrated a pragmatic response to changing circumstances?

*2 marks*

......................................................................................................................

......................................................................................................................

**2** How can beliefs in pragmatism and in tradition co-exist?

*2 marks*

......................................................................................................................

### Michael Oakeshott (1901–90)

| Ideas | Statements |
|---|---|
| • Human imperfection: the world is complex and to understand it is beyond the limits of human capability. Experience and tradition need to steer human conduct as we lack the rational capacity to interpret the world alone.<br>• Pragmatism: abstract ideas are feared, and experience and moderation act as a guide to human behaviour, leading to a pragmatic approach. | • 'To be conservative, then, is to prefer the familiar to the unknown, to prefer the tried to the untried, fact to mystery, the actual to the possible.'<br>• Need to ensure that 'the cure is not worse than the disease.' |

**3** Give TWO consequences of Oakeshott's view of human nature.

*2 marks*

......................................................................................................................

......................................................................................................................

**4** Why does Oakeshott support pragmatism? `3 marks`

......................................................................................................................................

......................................................................................................................................

......................................................................................................................................

## Tradition

Traditions are institutions or practices which have stood the test of time, demonstrating stability and continuity. Tradition is valued by conservatives, who believe it provides moral guidance, security and stability for psychologically imperfect humans.

Conservatives celebrate the traditional cultural elements in society. In the UK, the monarchy, the Church of England and religious festivals would be key examples. This links to the idea of an organic society, in which shared experiences and structures strengthen social integration. Within conservatism, neo-conservatives place a strong emphasis on tradition, in particular on traditional family values, which they believe provide the kind of moral guidance and authority needed for a secure society.

**5** What purpose do rules and conventions serve for conservatives? `4 marks`

......................................................................................................................................

......................................................................................................................................

......................................................................................................................................

......................................................................................................................................

**6** Why do neo-conservatives believe tradition to be important? `2 marks`

......................................................................................................................................

......................................................................................................................................

### Edmund Burke (1729–97)

| Ideas | Statements |
|---|---|
| • Change: writing at the time of the French Revolution, Burke argued that change was a necessary part of political survival but that it needed to be undertaken cautiously and with forethought. <br> • Tradition and empiricism: wisdom stems from the valuing of tradition and experience in society. This focus on the tried and tested ensures that society remains stable. | • 'Society is a partnership between the living, the dead, and the yet to be born.' <br> • 'A state without the means of some change is without the means of its own conservation.' |

**7** Explain Burke's views on change. `2 marks`

......................................................................................................................................

......................................................................................................................................

**8** Why is empiricism important for Burke? `2 marks`

......................................................................................................................................

......................................................................................................................................

15

## Human imperfection

A belief in human imperfection is at the heart of conservative thinking. There are three elements to this imperfection.

Humans are psychologically imperfect, which has implications for tradition and authority as humans are dependent and security seeking. Humans are also morally imperfect, with base and non-rational urges and instincts. This belief directs conservative views on law and order and traditional moral structures within society. Humans are intellectually imperfect, living in a world which is beyond human understanding. This explains the conservative preference for tradition, experience and pragmatism over fixed abstract principles, which require rational minds to interpret them.

However, neo-liberals perceive human nature differently, seeing rationality and positivity at the core of human nature.

**9** How do conservatives link human imperfection to tradition? `2 marks`

.........................................................................................................................................

.........................................................................................................................................

**10** What are the implications of the conservative belief that humans are intellectually imperfect? `3 marks`

.........................................................................................................................................

.........................................................................................................................................

.........................................................................................................................................

.........................................................................................................................................

## Organic society

For conservatives the organic society/state is more than just a collection of its individual parts. Each individual is part of, and contributes to, an organic whole. Duty, obligation and tradition act as the social cement that joins the whole together, and this is the spine of conservative thought. Shared values and a common culture ensure that the organic state flourishes; conservatives therefore fear diversity and pluralism as disruptive to the organic whole.

Hierarchy is implicit throughout the organic society: each element knows its place and inequality is natural. Indeed, conservatives argue that social equality is undesirable, impossible and ultimately unnatural. The organic society acts like a body, with different elements unequal (foot versus brain) but interdependent (they cannot exist in isolation). The success and flourishing of the whole is placed above each individual element.

**11** How does the conservative view of hierarchy support the concept of the organic society? `4 marks`

.........................................................................................................................................

.........................................................................................................................................

.........................................................................................................................................

.........................................................................................................................................

.........................................................................................................................................

**12** Why is inequality within society acceptable to conservatives? `2 marks`

.........................................................................................................................................

.........................................................................................................................................

## Thomas Hobbes (1588–1679)

| Ideas | Statements |
|---|---|
| • Order: an ordered, structured society is necessary to counteract the excesses of human nature and individualism. Without the order imposed by the state, which humans are obliged to support, anarchy would ensue.<br>• Human nature: all humans are ultimately weak and vulnerable, needing the security and stability that authority provides in order to thrive. Without this the human state of nature is chaotic and dangerous. | • 'The condition of man ... is the condition of war of everyone against everyone.'<br>• 'The life of man, solitary, poor, nasty, brutish and short.' |

**13** Why does Hobbes think life would be 'nasty, brutish and short'?    2 marks

..............................................................................................................................

..............................................................................................................................

**14** How does Hobbes view human nature?    2 marks

..............................................................................................................................

..............................................................................................................................

## Paternalism

The conservative belief in paternalism stems from the pragmatic belief that reform is preferable to revolution. Paternalism is the guidance and authority of those in positions of authority over the rest of society. Disraeli's response to the growing social inequalities of the Victorian period, and the potential unrest that these could provoke, was paternalistic. He offered a pragmatic response of qualified welfare to support the poorest in society, to quell discontent and to ensure that social stability and the natural hierarchy continued.

The moral argument for paternalism is based upon the conservative view of human imperfection, offering guidance and support for those who cannot act in their own interests. Finally, paternalism is linked to the concept of *noblesse oblige*: the idea that doing one's duty is the price paid for privilege and hierarchical position.

**15** Why did Disraeli develop the idea of paternalism?    4 marks

..............................................................................................................................

..............................................................................................................................

..............................................................................................................................

..............................................................................................................................

**16** How does paternalism link to the organic theory of society?    2 marks

..............................................................................................................................

..............................................................................................................................

## Libertarianism

Libertarianism is an element of some modern conservative thinking which is heavily influenced by liberal thinking, taking a more atomistic approach to individual achievement. Libertarian conservatism believes in the supremacy of the market and aims to liberate the economy from political regulation. This is based on a belief in the natural inequality of individuals in society; it is this belief that links libertarianism to conservatism. The cultural and institutional fabric of society is the context within which individuals interact for their own advantage. Libertarianism combines atomism with the desire for a society shaped by tradition and a shared culture, and is a core element of New Right thinking.

Libertarianism also featured in earlier conservative thinking which supported free trade and a self-regulating market. However, although conservatives have agreed with libertarian economic principles, this has not been extended to the social sphere where a strong state continues to be desirable.

**17** How do libertarian conservatives view the market? `2 marks`

...................................................................................................................................................

...................................................................................................................................................

...................................................................................................................................................

**18** How does libertarianism link to the core principles of conservatism? `4 marks`

...................................................................................................................................................

...................................................................................................................................................

...................................................................................................................................................

...................................................................................................................................................

...................................................................................................................................................

...................................................................................................................................................

### Robert Nozick (1938–2002)

| Ideas | Statements |
|---|---|
| • Libertarianism: liberty and individual rights are valued over other principles such as authority or organicism. Individual freedom is key and the state should be limited to ensure that this is so. <br> • Self-ownership: a commitment to individual rights and ownership means the state must not interfere with rewards for labour and talent. This would mean a small state with limited taxation. | • 'Individuals have rights and there are things no person or group may do to them (without violating their rights).' <br> • 'From each as they choose, to each as they are chosen.' <br> • 'No state more extensive than the minimal state can be justified.' |

**19** Give TWO ways in which Nozick's view of the individual differs from Hobbes'. `2 marks`

...................................................................................................................................................

...................................................................................................................................................

**20** What are the consequences of self-ownership? `2 marks`

...................................................................................................................................................

...................................................................................................................................................

### Ayn Rand (1905–82)

| Ideas | Statements |
|---|---|
| • Objectivism: the individual is completely free for Rand; atomist, rational and interested only in itself. The object is not the state but the individual. <br> • Freedom: Rand argued for a totally free market with a complete lack of government intervention and unregulated market competition. This would lead to a free market in its purest form. | • 'The only way a government can be of service to national prosperity is by keeping its hands off.' <br> • 'I am. I think. I will.' |

**21** What does Rand mean by *objectivism*? `2 marks`

.............................................................................................................................

.............................................................................................................................

**22** Give TWO features of Rand's free market. `2 marks`

.............................................................................................................................

.............................................................................................................................

# Differing views and tensions

## Traditional conservatism

Conservatism developed in reaction to Enlightenment thinking, which placed rationality and a positive view of human nature at the centre of what became liberal thought. The impact of the French Revolution, and the speed of political, social and economic change across Europe in the late eighteenth century, consolidated traditional conservative principles in response to this rapid change. Traditional conservatism was therefore based on empiricism — decision making based on what has been tried, tested and is known to work — rather than on hard principles, and on evolutionary, rather than revolutionary, change. Any change should be based on pragmatism rather than simply for principled reasons.

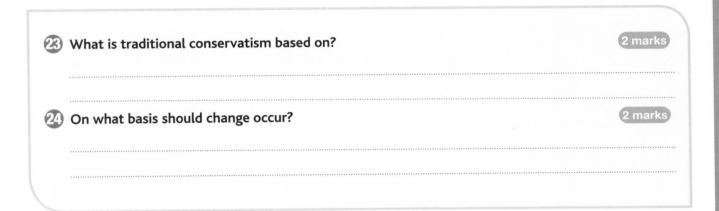

**23** What is traditional conservatism based on? `2 marks`

.............................................................................................................................

.............................................................................................................................

**24** On what basis should change occur? `2 marks`

.............................................................................................................................

.............................................................................................................................

## One-nation conservatism

Conservative pragmatism is best demonstrated by one-nation conservatism, which was Disraeli's response to growing social inequality and potentially revolutionary demands for reform. One-nation conservatism is paternalist, recognising that society is hierarchical but attaching social responsibility with the concept of *noblesse oblige*, where those at the top have a 'paternal' responsibility towards those at the bottom.

Disraeli's social and political reforms, in effect legislative paternalism, helped to ensure that Britain did not experience the revolutions that swept across Europe in the nineteenth century. This one-nation conservatism can be seen at other points in British political history, including the years after the Second World War, when a managed economy, as advocated by Keynes, and welfare state were desirable to achieve full employment and maintain social stability.

**25** What is the link between paternalism and one-nation conservatism? `2 marks`

.............................................................................................................................

.............................................................................................................................

**26** Give TWO examples of one-nation conservatism.

2 marks

..................................................................................................................................

..................................................................................................................................

..................................................................................................................................

## New Right conservatism

New Right conservatism developed in the 1970s as a response to the managed economy and developed welfare state of the post-war period. It critiques 'big government' and aims to challenge egalitarianism, confirming the traditional conservative belief in hierarchy, albeit a more meritocratic version. The New Right also aims to reduce the expectation of what governments can and should do. There are two core strands to New Right conservatism: neo-liberal (largely focused on the economy) and neo-conservative (focused on the social sphere), which are apparently contradictory as they have contrasting ideological heritages. However, shared views on the role of government and a common desire to return to a golden, pre-reform age mean that the two strands are not in complete opposition to each other.

**27** Why did New Right conservatism develop?

2 marks

..................................................................................................................................

..................................................................................................................................

**28** Are the two strands of New Right conservatism in complete opposition to each other?

4 marks

..................................................................................................................................

..................................................................................................................................

..................................................................................................................................

..................................................................................................................................

..................................................................................................................................

..................................................................................................................................

## Neo-liberalism

Neo-liberalism is an updated version of classical liberalism which is focused on the defence of individual economic freedom through the free market and the reduction of state intervention. This means deregulation and privatisation with no state control over how the market works or its outcomes. In social terms neo-liberals are anti-welfarist, arguing that welfare creates a dependency culture that reduces the efficiency of the market. Individuals should be responsible for helping themselves, rather than the state doing so.

As neo-liberalism stems from classical liberalism it promotes the individual and has a mechanistic view of society. Human nature is viewed positively, with humans seen as rational and capable of the decision making that a free market requires. The hierarchy of traditional conservatism is redefined as a meritocratic ladder where hard work and effort are rewarded with success and status. Taxation is viewed negatively by neo-liberals, who argue that the state should not profit from an individual's hard work. Indeed, taxation to fund welfare payments, in contrast to the paternalism of one-nation conservatives, is seen as legalised theft. Rather than being pragmatic, neo-liberalism is ideological and has clear doctrinal principles.

**29** How do neo-liberals view human nature?

2 marks

**30** What are the neo-liberal criticisms of welfare?

2 marks

**31** What does a neo-liberal market look like?

4 marks

## Neo-conservatism

Although neo-conservatism shares a desire to limit the size of the state, it has not adopted a neo-liberal libertarian approach to the social sphere. It is a largely authoritarian principle, taking a strongly moral, anti-permissive, faith-based approach to, for example, family values. This moral revivalism was a reaction to permissiveness and to the freedoms gained from the 1960s onwards by women and other social groups, leading to a perceived decline in the structure of society. This authoritarian approach can also be seen in the desire for strong law and order, which reflects attitudes to human imperfection which neo-conservatives share with traditional conservatives. Natural inequality is defended by neo-conservatives, who celebrate hierarchy and traditional forms of authority. Neo-conservatism, like neo-liberalism, has clear principles and in this it differs from traditional conservatism's pragmatic approach.

Another key area of neo-conservative focus is nationalism, with patriotism providing a sense of stability and security for the organic society. This is an exclusive attitude that can manifest itself in insularity and often xenophobia. At the heart of neo-conservatism is a belief that faith, family and nation are vital elements of the moral fabric of society.

**32** What are neo-conservatives reacting against?

2 marks

**33** Why do neo-conservatives believe in strong law and order?

2 marks

**34** How does the neo-conservative celebration of nationalism manifest itself?

2 marks

## Summary table

**35** Fill in the table.

| | Liberal New Right | Conservative New Right |
|---|---|---|
| Roots | | |
| Focus (economic/social) | | |
| Examples | | |
| Focus (individual/community) | | |
| Examples | | |
| Key theorists and figures | | |

## Exam-style questions

**1** To what extent are conservatives pragmatic? You must use appropriate thinkers you have studied to support your answer. ⏱ **35** (24 marks)

*In the introduction, outline what is meant by the term pragmatic. Are some strands of conservatism more or less pragmatic than others?*

.................................................................................................
.................................................................................................
.................................................................................................
.................................................................................................
.................................................................................................
.................................................................................................

*Paragraph 1. Traditional conservatives favour pragmatism. Link to views on human nature and empiricism. Thinker: Hobbes.*

........................................................................................................................................................................

........................................................................................................................................................................

........................................................................................................................................................................

........................................................................................................................................................................

........................................................................................................................................................................

........................................................................................................................................................................

*Paragraph 2. One-nation conservatism was a pragmatic response to changing circumstances. Think about social reforms and idea of* noblesse oblige. *Thinker: Burke.*

........................................................................................................................................................................

........................................................................................................................................................................

........................................................................................................................................................................

........................................................................................................................................................................

........................................................................................................................................................................

........................................................................................................................................................................

........................................................................................................................................................................

*Paragraph 3. Elements of neo-conservatism are pragmatic. Authoritarian response to changing social circumstances. Thinker: Oakeshott.*

........................................................................................................................................................................

........................................................................................................................................................................

........................................................................................................................................................................

........................................................................................................................................................................

........................................................................................................................................................................

........................................................................................................................................................................

*Paragraph 4. Strands within conservatism favour principles over pragmatism. Consider the approaches of libertarianism. Thinker: Rand.*

........................................................................................................................................................................

........................................................................................................................................................................

........................................................................................................................................................................

........................................................................................................................................................................

........................................................................................................................................................................

........................................................................................................................................................................

........................................................................................................................................................................

*Paragraph 5. The New Right is largely principled with a focus on economic liberty and free market capitalism. It takes a more positive view of human nature. Thinker: Noyzick.*

.................................................................................................................................
.................................................................................................................................
.................................................................................................................................
.................................................................................................................................
.................................................................................................................................
.................................................................................................................................
.................................................................................................................................
.................................................................................................................................

**Conclusion. Weigh up the evidence. Is conservatism merely a pragmatic response to changing circumstances? Is pragmatism in itself an ideological principle? Has conservatism evolved away from pragmatism?**

.................................................................................................................................
.................................................................................................................................
.................................................................................................................................
.................................................................................................................................
.................................................................................................................................
.................................................................................................................................
.................................................................................................................................
.................................................................................................................................

**2** **To what extent do conservatives differ over the role of the state? You must use appropriate thinkers you have studied to support your answer.**

**35** **24 marks**

*Plan your answer below and write your essay on a separate sheet of paper.*

.................................................................................................................................
.................................................................................................................................
.................................................................................................................................
.................................................................................................................................
.................................................................................................................................
.................................................................................................................................
.................................................................................................................................
.................................................................................................................................
.................................................................................................................................
.................................................................................................................................
.................................................................................................................................
.................................................................................................................................

# Topic 3

## Socialism

Socialism developed as an ideology as a result of the profound and obvious inequalities created by the Industrial Revolution and the advent of free market capitalism. Poverty, inequality and exploitation combined with the absence of democracy and rights led to the development of a set of ideas that aimed to create a fair and equal society.

## Core ideas and principles

### Equality

Equality is the fundamental value identifying all socialists. By equality, socialists are referring to equality of outcome, based on the redistribution of resources. This, socialists argue, will result in fairness and justice, with all able to be free in the positive sense to achieve personal goals and to make full use of their abilities and talents. Equality also leads to cooperation and fraternity between individuals, and a decline of conflict in society.

> **1** Give TWO reasons for the socialist belief in equality of outcome. **2 marks**
>
> ................................................................................
>
> ................................................................................

Socialists reject meritocracy, arguing that it will lead to further inequality, with most losing out in the competition for success. They believe that the structure of society is profoundly unfair, with some starting life with huge inherited privileges. This means that any forms of equality other than outcome will be inadequate and unfair to those who were not born with advantages. This links closely to the socialist critique of capitalism, which is an economic system that leads to winners and losers as a result of inherited wealth and the accumulation of private property. However, there is some division within socialism over whether the aim should be to achieve absolute equality or simply to narrow the divisions between rich and poor.

> **2** How do socialists criticise the liberal belief in equality of opportunity and meritocracy? **3 marks**
>
> ................................................................................
>
> ................................................................................
>
> ................................................................................
>
> ................................................................................
>
> **3** Outline THREE features of capitalism. **2 marks**
>
> ................................................................................
>
> ................................................................................
>
> ................................................................................

## Common humanity

Socialists believe in the idea of common humanity, arguing that human nature is essentially social, that links and connections between people are strong, and that cooperation is natural. In contrast, they see competition as something forced on us by capitalism, driving us to act against our essential natures and making most people unhappy and frustrated.

Socialists argue that human behaviour is changeable and can be improved upon, leading to the utopian possibility of human improvement and perfectibility within a future socialist society. This is one of the reasons why socialism is seen as a highly optimistic ideology.

**4** **What is meant by the term *fraternity*?** `1 mark`

................................................................................................

**5** **Describe why socialists believe that cooperation is natural.** `3 marks`

................................................................................................

................................................................................................

................................................................................................

**6** **What is meant by *utopianism* and how can socialism be seen as utopian?** `5 marks`

................................................................................................

................................................................................................

................................................................................................

................................................................................................

................................................................................................

................................................................................................

## Social class

Social class is another key socialist concern. This means the way in which society is subdivided based on socioeconomic circumstances. Capitalism, according to socialists, has created these structures. Marxists believe that there are only two social classes, the bourgeoisie (the owners of production) and the proletariat (the vast majority — 99.9%), therefore defining class in purely economic terms. Once members of the proletariat have become class conscious — aware of their links to others with similar economic circumstances — they will rise up against the bourgeoisie in a mass revolutionary movement.

**7** **Why is social class significant for socialists?** `4 marks`

................................................................................................

................................................................................................

................................................................................................

................................................................................................

Socialism has been seen as an ideology which aims to represent the working class in its struggle for equality. Social democrats are less focused on the role of class, hoping to win the votes of all classes, rather than just the industrial working class, which shrank due to the decline in heavy industry in twentieth-century Western Europe.

### Karl Marx (1818–83) and Friedrich Engels (1820–95)

| Ideas | Statements |
|---|---|
| • Social class: all societies in history are based on the economic relations between two unequal classes, one ruling and one subordinate. Class conflict is at the heart of all societies.<br>• Human nature is plastic and malleable. People are the product of society and social conditioning. Our true natures will only be revealed after the end of capitalism, when we live in a completely equal society. | • 'Workers of the world unite, you have nothing to lose but your chains.'<br>• 'From each according to his ability, to each according to his needs.' |

## Workers' control

Socialists have developed a range of ways to replace or tame capitalism. Marxists favour common ownership, which in communist countries such as the USSR has tended to mean state control of the means of production.

Social democrats favour a more limited response, which does not involve the state controlling all aspects of the economy, but trade unions have always been at the heart of the socialist movement. This leads to the idea of workers' control, where the workers take over the control and running of the means of production — an alternative to both state control and capitalism.

**8** **What do socialists mean by *common ownership*?**  `3 marks`

.......................................................................................................................................

.......................................................................................................................................

**9** **What is the implication of common ownership for the role of the state?**  `1 mark`

.......................................................................................................................................

**10** **What is a trade union and why are unions linked to socialism?**  `3 marks`

.......................................................................................................................................

.......................................................................................................................................

.......................................................................................................................................

## Collectivism

Collectivism rather than individualism is another key belief of all socialists. Collectivism implies that working together in order to achieve the common good is both morally and practically preferable to individual competitive striving.

**11** **Distinguish between *collectivism* and *individualism*.**  `3 marks`

.......................................................................................................................................

.......................................................................................................................................

.......................................................................................................................................

.......................................................................................................................................

Collectivism and cooperation are seen as coming naturally to humans, as we are social and empathetic. Socialists also see collectivism as more efficient and less wasteful. They argue that people are more productive when working alongside others for the collective good, rather than against each other for monetary gain. Individualism is seen to create unhappiness, division and conflict in society.

Socialists therefore seek collectivist solutions to social and economic problems, although different methods have been suggested by different types of socialist. Communists have seen the state as operating on behalf of the people as the collective body, which could include state control of the economy and nationalisation. Social democrats have favoured the use of the welfare state, where all contribute and all benefit.

**12** Outline three features of communism.

3 marks

..................................................................................................

..................................................................................................

..................................................................................................

**13** Identify THREE contrasting examples of ways that socialists have put collectivism into practice.

3 marks

..................................................................................................

..................................................................................................

..................................................................................................

**14** What are the implications of collectivism for the economy?

3 marks

..................................................................................................

..................................................................................................

..................................................................................................

# Differing views and tensions

## Revolutionary socialism

Revolutionary socialism (or Marxism) was very popular in nineteenth- and early twentieth-century Europe, when few had the vote and workers lacked other political and social rights. This form of socialism has both radical means and ends. Marx argued that class conflict was at the heart of all societies throughout history. Every stage in history consisted of one class exploiting another, which eventually led to the demise of that stage or epoch. The harsh inequalities created by the latest stage in history, capitalism, would inevitably result in an uprising of the proletariat (wage earners) against the bourgeoisie (owners of production) resulting in a revolution. Capitalism, Marx believed, was inherently unstable and contained the roots of its own demise. In order to create profit for the owners of the means of production, the working-class majority must be exploited and underpaid for the fruits of their labour.

**15** Why do Marxists wish to overthrow capitalism?

2 marks

..................................................................................................

..................................................................................................

Marx believed that eventually the workers would become class conscious, form a mass movement and overthrow capitalism. Reform was seen as pointless as the state represented the interests of the bourgeoisie and any changes introduced would simply be window dressing.

**16** What is meant by the term *class consciousness*?  `1 mark`

...................................................................................................

...................................................................................................

**17** Explain Marx's theory of historical materialism.  `2 marks`

...................................................................................................

...................................................................................................

**18** What is meant by the term *dialectic*?  `2 marks`

...................................................................................................

...................................................................................................

...................................................................................................

After the revolution, there would be a temporary workers' state — the dictatorship of the proletariat — in order to protect the revolution from its enemies. During this stage, capitalism and private property would be abolished and there would be redistribution of wealth, resulting in equality of outcome. Once this was achieved, there would be no need for a state and it would simply wither away, as everyone would have their needs met and would be able to fulfil their goals.

**19** Outline FIVE elements of Marxist thought.  `5 marks`

...................................................................................................

...................................................................................................

...................................................................................................

...................................................................................................

...................................................................................................

### Rosa Luxemburg (1871–1919)

| Ideas | Statements |
|---|---|
| • Rejection of gradualism: social democracy would involve an acceptance of capitalism. Capitalism will always result in the exploitation of the proletariat, so must be abolished.<br>• The role of class consciousness: as social democracy developed, workers would spontaneously become class conscious, resulting in a mass movement. | • 'Social democracy ... is only the advance guard of the proletariat.'<br>• 'The masses are the decisive element; they are the rock on which the final victory of the revolution will be built.' |

**20** Define the following Marxist terms.  `5 marks`

a *Surplus value* ...................................................................................

b *Bourgeoisie* .....................................................................................

c *Proletariat* .......................................................................................

d *Alienation* .......................................................................................

e *Class conflict* ...................................................................................

**21** Explain Marx's argument that communism was inevitable. `4 marks`

........................................................................................

........................................................................................

........................................................................................

........................................................................................

**22** How did Rosa Luxemburg criticise social democracy? `2 marks`

........................................................................................

........................................................................................

## Evolutionary socialism

Evolutionary socialism developed at the start of the twentieth century. Eduard Bernstein argued that capitalism had matured, and proven more complex and less unstable than Marx had predicted. With the introduction of universal male suffrage in many Western European nations, the legalisation of trade unions and the introduction of other rights, workers had become integrated in society, their living standards were improving and violent revolution was no longer necessary or desirable.

**23** Identify TWO ways in which evolutionary socialism differs from revolutionary socialism. `2 marks`

........................................................................................

........................................................................................

Gradualists such as the Fabians believed that parliamentary democracy and representative government were the best ways to introduce socialist reforms, and were unimpressed by the authoritarian systems that developed after revolutions in China and the USSR.

### Beatrice Webb (1858–1943)

| Ideas | Statements |
| --- | --- |
| • Gradualism: the belief that socialism is best achieved through the existing democratic political system and the introduction of social reforms. Education and persuasion would lead the majority of the population to support these measures.<br>• The role of the state: the democratic state is a neutral body which can be harnessed to introduce socialism and transform society. This would involve the creation of a welfare state using progressive taxation. | • 'Nature still obstinately refuses to cooperate by making the rich people innately superior to the poor people.' |

**24** What is meant by the term *revisionism*? `1 mark`

........................................................................................

**25** Explain TWO reasons why some socialists rejected Marxism and embraced gradualism and revisionism. `2 marks`

........................................................................................

........................................................................................

**26** Why did reformist socialists like Beatrice Webb argue that gradualism was inevitable? Describe FOUR stages of the process by which gradualism would achieve its aims. `4 marks`

..................................................................................................

..................................................................................................

..................................................................................................

..................................................................................................

## Social democracy

Social democracy, or reformist/revisionist socialism, developed during the twentieth century alongside the development of gradualism. Social democrats do not reject capitalism, seeking instead to tame and control it.

First, the wealth generated by capitalism can be captured by the state and redistributed to the citizens via a progressive tax system and a universal 'cradle to grave' welfare state. This would reduce the divisions between rich and poor, leading to a more equal society.

**27** Why do social democrats accept capitalism? `2 marks`

..................................................................................................

..................................................................................................

..................................................................................................

Second, social democrats reject the communist planned economy, instead favouring a mixed economy, with key industries such as railways, water and electricity controlled by the state and other areas of the economy controlled by the private sector. The state plays a key role in intervening in the economy in order to humanise and control capitalism, for example by introducing wide-ranging regulations on business. Social democrats, as gradualists, believe that peaceful persuasion and gradual reform through the political system is the only democratic way to create a socialist society.

**28** Outline THREE aspects of Keynesian economics. `3 marks`

..................................................................................................

..................................................................................................

**29** How does Keynesian economics differ from the economic analysis of Karl Marx? `3 marks`

..................................................................................................

..................................................................................................

**30** Outline THREE similarities in Marxist and social democratic thought. `3 marks`

..................................................................................................

..................................................................................................

**31** Outline THREE differences between Marxists and social democrats. `3 marks`

.............................................................................................................................................

.............................................................................................................................................

.............................................................................................................................................

**32** What is meant by the term *social justice*? `1 mark`

.............................................................................................................................................

.............................................................................................................................................

## Anthony Crosland (1918–77)

| Ideas | Statements |
|---|---|
| • Managed capitalism: capitalism should be allowed to flourish as long as it does not exploit the vulnerable. The wealth created by capitalism can be redistributed to create a more equal society.<br>• The mixed economy and the welfare state, along with a progressive tax system, are the key to creating a more equal, fair and just system. | • 'Nationalisation ... does not in itself engender greater equality.' |

**33** Explain Crosland's view of capitalism. `2 marks`

.............................................................................................................................................

.............................................................................................................................................

.............................................................................................................................................

The third way, or neo-revisionism, developed as a pragmatic reaction to the rise of the New Right in the 1980s and the success of politicians such as Margaret Thatcher. This approach is arguably not a form of socialism at all, but closer to modern liberalism. Third way supporters such as Tony Blair praise the success of capitalism and want a reduced role for the state, accepting and even supporting privatisation. The term 'third way' implies that supporters reject both free market capitalism and state socialism. Although still seeking a more equal and fair society, supporters of the third way believe the private sector can have a role in achieving this, possibly working alongside the public sector in a partnership.

## Anthony Giddens (1938–)

| Ideas | Statements |
|---|---|
| • The free market can carry out many of the roles previously carried out by the state, or can work in cooperation with it.<br>• Reduced state intervention: the state's focus should be on investment in education, training and infrastructure in order to stimulate the economy. | • 'The new mixed economy looks ... for a synergy between public and private sectors.' |

**34** What is the role of the state, according to Anthony Giddens? `1 mark`

.............................................................................................................................................

.............................................................................................................................................

**35** Outline THREE differences between a revisionist socialist and a supporter of the third way.

3 marks

..................................................................................................................................

..................................................................................................................................

..................................................................................................................................

**36** Outline THREE similarities between a revisionist socialist and a supporter of the third way.

3 marks

..................................................................................................................................

..................................................................................................................................

..................................................................................................................................

## Summary table

**37** Fill in the table.

| | State | Economy | Society |
|---|---|---|---|
| Revolutionary socialism | | | |
| Social democracy | | | |
| Third way | | | |

**38** Outline the impact of the following historical events in the twentieth century on socialism.

| Event | Impact on socialism |
|---|---|
| Russian Revolution, 1917 | |
| Universal suffrage in the UK, 1918/28 | |
| Creation of the welfare state in the UK, 1944–50 | |
| Cold War, 1945–90 | |
| Rise of the New Right and election of Margaret Thatcher as PM in 1979 | |
| Collapse of communism after 1989 | |
| Election of Tony Blair as PM in 1997 | |
| Another event of your choice | |

## Exam-style questions

**1** To what extent do socialists agree on both the means and ends of socialism? You must use appropriate thinkers you have studied to support your answer.

(35) **24 marks**

*In the introduction, outline what is meant by 'the means and ends'. Has division been a big problem in the socialist movement?*

......................................................................................................................

......................................................................................................................

......................................................................................................................

*Paragraph 1. Socialists do not agree on the means, although the division has reduced since the fall of communism. Revolutionary socialists believe in a mass uprising of the proletariat. Thinkers: Marx, Engels, Luxemburg.*

......................................................................................................................

......................................................................................................................

......................................................................................................................

*Paragraph 2. In contrast to revolutionaries, evolutionary socialists believe in gradualism and slow change through the parliamentary process. Thinkers: Webb, Crosland.*

......................................................................................................................................................
......................................................................................................................................................
......................................................................................................................................................
......................................................................................................................................................

*Paragraph 3. Since the early twentieth century socialists have not agreed on the ends. Marxists believe in equality of outcome and the abolition of capitalism because...*
*Thinkers: Luxemburg and Marx.*

......................................................................................................................................................
......................................................................................................................................................
......................................................................................................................................................
......................................................................................................................................................

*Paragraph 4. Social democrats do not fully reject capitalism and believe in reducing rather than eradicating equality. Thinkers: Webb and Crosland.*

......................................................................................................................................................
......................................................................................................................................................
......................................................................................................................................................
......................................................................................................................................................

*Paragraph 5. Neo-revisionists go further, accepting and supporting capitalism and the free market. They also accept individualism to some extent. Thinker: Giddens.*

......................................................................................................................................................
......................................................................................................................................................
......................................................................................................................................................
......................................................................................................................................................

*Paragraph 6. However, there are some core values that unite all socialists.*

......................................................................................................................................................
......................................................................................................................................................
......................................................................................................................................................
......................................................................................................................................................

*Conclusion. Weigh up the evidence. With the decline of radical revolutionary socialism, do socialists now agree on the means and the ends? Make sure you address both aspects of the question and include important dates.*

......................................................................................................................................................
......................................................................................................................................................
......................................................................................................................................................
......................................................................................................................................................

**2** To what extent are socialists committed to the abolition of capitalism? You must use appropriate thinkers you have studied to support your answer.

*Plan your answer below and write your essay on a separate sheet of paper.*

35 **24 marks**

# Topic 4

## Feminism

## Core ideas and principles

Feminism developed during the nineteenth and twentieth centuries after writers such as Mary Wollstonecraft began to apply Enlightenment principles to women as well as men. This developed into campaigns for the vote in the early twentieth century. In the 1960s, second-wave feminism argued that despite legal rights women were still dissatisfied and discriminated against, and radical feminists argued that the debate must now turn to the family and private life. Modern feminism is a flourishing but divided ideology.

**1** **Outline how and why feminism developed as an ideology.** `5 marks`

........................................................................................................

........................................................................................................

........................................................................................................

........................................................................................................

### Sex and gender

Anti-feminists often presume that sex and gender are interchangeable terms. Feminists argue that while sex is a biological term, gender is a social construct. We learn our gender roles from the society we grow up in. For example, girls are taught that it is important to care for their appearance, while boys are encouraged to be active and sporty. This means that gender is not fixed, and ideas about gender can change. Biology is therefore not destiny: just because a woman can have a baby, it does not mean that she has to have one, or if she does, that she has to be responsible for the childrearing.

**2** **Explain the term *gender stereotype* and give TWO examples.** `3 marks`

........................................................................................................

........................................................................................................

**3** **What do feminists mean when they argue that sex and gender have different meanings, and why is this difference significant?** `5 marks`

........................................................................................................

........................................................................................................

........................................................................................................

........................................................................................................

........................................................................................................

## Simone de Beauvoir (1908–86)

| Ideas | Statements |
|---|---|
| • Women are different from men because they have been taught and socialised to be different. *The Second Sex* explores de Beauvoir's realisation of the many ways in which her life had been affected by having been born a girl.<br>• De Beauvoir also explored the theory of 'otherness' — that men are seen as 'normal' humans while women are seen as deviant or abnormal. Women then internalise this sense of inferiority and are oppressed not only by patriarchy, but by themselves. | • 'One is not born, but rather becomes, a woman.'<br>• 'Man is defined as a human being and woman as a female — whenever she behaves as a human being she is said to imitate the male.' |

**4** **What does de Beauvoir mean by the term *otherness*?**  `1 mark`

.........................................................................................................................................

.........................................................................................................................................

**5** **What does de Beauvoir mean by 'One is not born, but rather becomes, a woman'?**  `2 marks`

.........................................................................................................................................

.........................................................................................................................................

.........................................................................................................................................

## Patriarchy

Feminists do not see women's inequality as natural. It is the result of an artificial construct, patriarchy, meaning rule by men. The aim of feminism is therefore to overthrow patriarchy and create a more equal and fair society. Liberal feminists focus on patriarchy in the institutions of the public sphere, holding women back from equality in education, work and politics. Socialist feminists examine the relationship between capitalism and patriarchy and argue that they depend on each other. Radical feminists see patriarchy as far more complex and pervasive, as rooted deep within the nuclear family structure and in the personal and intimate relationships between men and women.

**6** **Complete the table.**  `6 marks`

| Type of feminist | Interpretation of patriarchy | Implications for the role of the state |
|---|---|---|
| Liberal | | |
| Socialist | | |
| Radical | | |

## Charlotte Perkins Gilman (1860–1935)

| Ideas | Statements |
|---|---|
| • Gilman argued that women should be allowed economic independence and wrote about reforming the family and marriage in order to free women from the burden of childrearing. She saw marriage and domestic life as confining and restrictive and attacked the societal norms that defined women in such narrow ways.<br>• Gilman explored ideas such as communal childcare. Her book *Herland* imagined a world without men. | • 'There is no female mind. The brain is not an organ of sex. Might as well speak of a female liver.'<br>• 'It is not that women are really smaller-minded, weaker-minded, more timid ... but that whosoever ... lives in a small, dark place, is always guarded, protected, directed and restrained, will become inevitably narrowed and weakened by it.' |

**7** According to Gilman, why were women unequal in nineteenth-century America?  **1 mark**

.................................................................................................

.................................................................................................

## 'The personal is political'

This famous slogan is crucial to an understanding of feminism. It seeks to destroy the Victorian idea of separate spheres: the private, where woman take care of the home and children, and the public, where men can make law, work and learn. This division of society suggests that everything that happens in the privacy of the home is not political but natural. It also keeps women from entering the public world of politics, work and education, suggesting that this is both against their nature and potentially socially disruptive. By ending this artificial division, feminists create a new interpretation of what politics itself means: from something that happens between men in the public world, to something that exists wherever there are 'power-structured relationships' (Kate Millett).

**8** Outline what feminists mean by the *public* and *private spheres*.  **2 marks**

.................................................................................................

**9** Why do radical feminists use the slogan 'the personal is political'?  **2 marks**

.................................................................................................

.................................................................................................

**10** Why do liberal feminists have concerns about the slogan 'the personal is political'?  **2 marks**

.................................................................................................

.................................................................................................

.................................................................................................

## Equality feminism

Most feminists believe that women should be equal to men and this was the aim of all feminists until the 1960s. By equality, feminists mean that women should have the same rights and opportunities as men in work, education and politics, for example. Equality (or egalitarian) feminists believe that differences in biology have little impact on our character and we are all products of our environment and social conditioning. Men and women are seen as naturally androgynous, and equality feminists aim to return to androgyny, where sex is irrelevant and gender stereotypes cease to exist. This form of feminism has been advocated by liberal, socialist and some radical feminists.

**11** What do feminists mean by the term *androgyny*?

1 mark

..................................................................................................................................

**12** Outline THREE key arguments of equality feminism.

3 marks

..................................................................................................................................

..................................................................................................................................

..................................................................................................................................

..................................................................................................................................

## Difference feminism

In the 1960s some radical feminists developed a critique of the idea of equality between men and women. They argued that equality implied women should be more like men, and take on male characteristics such as aggression, promiscuity and competitiveness, in order to compete with them in the public sphere. Difference feminists argued that women would become 'male identified', accepting of patriarchy itself, and lose their essential essence. Some difference feminists argued that women's ability to create and sustain life through pregnancy, childbirth and breast feeding, makes them more empathetic and creative than men, leading them to argue that women are in fact superior to men and that the two sexes are fundamentally incompatible. Living separately from men was suggested as a solution in some cases.

**13** What do difference feminists mean by the term *essentialism*?

1 mark

..................................................................................................................................

**14** Outline THREE key arguments of difference feminism.

3 marks

..................................................................................................................................

..................................................................................................................................

..................................................................................................................................

..................................................................................................................................

**15** How would an equality feminist criticise a difference feminist?

2 marks

..................................................................................................................................

..................................................................................................................................

**16** How would a difference feminist criticise an equality feminist?

2 marks

..................................................................................................................................

..................................................................................................................................

..................................................................................................................................

**17** Outline the different ways in which feminists view human nature. `3 marks`

## Intersectionality

Black feminists such as bell hooks have criticised other forms of feminism, particularly liberal feminism, for making generalisations about women's experiences and claiming to speak for all women, despite being overwhelmingly white, middle-class and western.

Intersectionality proposes that women experience many different and complex layers of oppression, such as racism and ageism, as well as sexism. For example, the family — a source of patriarchal oppression according to many feminists — can be a haven from racism for many black women and a source of empowerment.

### bell hooks (1952–)

| Ideas | Statements |
|---|---|
| hooks examines the intersectionality of ethnicity, gender, class and other potential forms of oppression. Commenting on the dominance of white middle-class women in feminism, she argues that there are many interlinked forms of oppression that are experienced by different women in different ways. She also argues that the feminist mass movement must open up to include women from a much wider range of backgrounds, and that men should also be allowed to join feminist movements. | • 'If I were asked to define myself, I wouldn't start with race; I wouldn't start with blackness; I wouldn't start with gender; I wouldn't start with feminism.'<br>• 'Feminism is for everybody.' |

**18** Explain the meaning of the term *intersectionality*. `2 marks`

**19** How is intersectionality used as a criticism of the mainstream liberal feminist movement? `3 marks`

# Differing views and tensions

## Liberal feminism

Liberal feminists extend liberal ideas about the freedom and autonomy of the individual to women as well as men. This form of feminism has its roots in the nineteenth- and early twentieth-century campaigns for the vote and other legal reforms. It was revived in the 1960s by writers such as Betty Friedan.

Liberal feminists argue that one's gender is insignificant, as each person should be judged on their character, effort and talent rather than their biology. As individualists, they aim to create a gender-blind society, and for women and men to achieve 'personhood', where gender and sex cease to matter. These individuals can then compete on an equal basis. Liberal feminist campaigners have had great successes in parts of the western world in opening up the public sphere of work, education and politics to women. However, as liberals, they fear the tyranny of the interventionist state and therefore do not wish to interfere in the private relationships between men and women, seeing them as an area of personal choice and freedom.

**20** **Complete the table.**  6 marks

| Liberal idea | Implications for liberal feminism |
|---|---|
| Rationality and reason | |
| Individualism | |
| Equality of opportunity | |
| Reform | |
| Limited state | |
| Choice and freedom | |

**21** **In the context of feminism, what is meant by the term *discrimination*?**  1 mark

......................................................................................................................................................................

**22** Suggest two current examples of gender discrimination.  `2 marks`

**23** What do liberal feminists mean by *political* and *legal equality*?  `2 marks`

**24** How is liberal feminism criticised by radical, socialist and black feminists?  `6 marks`

## Socialist feminism

Socialist feminists argue that the roots of patriarchy are closely linked to capitalism. They see connections between the desire for profit, and the need to keep women inferior and confined to domestic labour and childcare. Capitalism, argued Engels, led to urbanisation and the development of the privatised nuclear family. The growing significance of private property led to inheritance passing through the eldest son, excluding and devaluing women. The male breadwinner is forced to work long hours for little pay in order to provide for his family, while the housewife provides the 'warm bath' — the comforts of home — in order to relieve his stress and ensure that he is back at work the following day to be exploited further. Marxist feminists have argued that women should focus on class-based movements, and that this will lead to the destruction of patriarchy as well as capitalism. Modern socialist feminists such as Sheila Rowbotham argue that patriarchy predates capitalism, and that they are interlinked forms of oppression for working-class women.

**25** How do socialist feminists link capitalism to patriarchy?  `2 marks`

**26** What did Engels mean by describing women as the 'reserve army of labour'?  `2 marks`

**27** How has socialist feminism been criticised by other feminists?  `2 marks`

### Sheila Rowbotham (1943–)

| Ideas | Statements |
|---|---|
| • Socialist feminist Rowbotham has focused on the links between class- and gender-based oppression. She was one of the pioneers of the women's liberation movement in the UK, with its demands for equal pay, education and opportunity, 24-hour nurseries, free contraception and abortion on demand.<br>• Rowbotham argues that women will only achieve liberation in an egalitarian socialist society, without the exploitation of the free market. | • 'There is a difference between having your own movement and cutting yourself off from other movements.'<br>• 'The revolutionary woman knows the world she seeks to overthrow is precisely one in which love between equal human beings is well nigh impossible.'<br>• 'Men will often admit that other women are oppressed but not you.' |

 **28** How does Sheila Rowbotham link capitalism to the oppression of women in both the home and public spheres?  **2 marks**

..................................................................................................................................

..................................................................................................................................

## Radical feminism

Radical feminists argue that gender is the greatest social divide in all societies, with more significance than class, ethnicity, age or any other division. In stark contrast to liberal feminists, they argue that patriarchy is rooted in the nuclear family, in the way we raise our children and in the personal relations between men and women. Reforming the public sphere will therefore only scratch the surface, leaving patriarchy unchallenged. Radical feminists have suggested a wide range of methods to end patriarchy, including separatism — women choosing to live apart from men — and the use of technology to help women avoid pregnancy and childbirth.

Unlike other forms of feminism, radical feminism has no links to other ideologies, and in its focus on gender and reinterpretation of politics, it is profoundly different. It is a broad movement, including both equality feminists, who see gender as ceasing to have relevance or meaning, and difference feminists, who see equality as a limited aim and suggest women should celebrate their differences in order to be truly liberated.

### Kate Millett (1934–2017)

| Ideas | Statements |
|---|---|
| • Kate Millett's book *Sexual Politics* (1970) arguably started the radical feminist movement. It argued that patriarchy was not just embedded in the public world of education, work and politics, but was in fact far more pervasive and rooted in the personal and domestic life of the family. The socialisation of children into patriarchal ideology in the home is subsequently strengthened in the public world by the media, school, peers, etc.<br>• *Sexual Politics* also examined the deep-rooted misogyny present in the work of many celebrated twentieth-century male writers, such as Norman Mailer and D. H. Lawrence. | • 'The great mass of women throughout history have been confined to the cultural level of animal life in providing the male with sexual outlet and exercising the animal functions of reproduction and care for the young.'<br>• 'The lesbian is the archetypical feminist, because she's not into men — she's the independent woman par excellence.' |

**29** Explain Kate Millett's view of the traditional nuclear family and its link to patriarchy.  **2 marks**

..................................................................................................................................

..................................................................................................................................

**30** How has radical feminism been criticised by other feminists?    4 marks

........................................................................................................................

........................................................................................................................

........................................................................................................................

........................................................................................................................

## Postmodern feminism

Postmodern feminists argue that, like all 'isms', feminism is a generalisation. Even the term 'woman' is possibly meaningless, as some women cannot have children and do not even have wombs, so what is it that actually defines being a woman? Postmodern feminists argue that women's experiences are very varied, depending on nationality, age, sexuality and ethnicity, for example. Patriarchy manifests itself differently and there is no one 'true' experience. Postmodern feminists have often examined the way language is used to construct ideas about gender; as a result they have been seen as elitist and neglectful of more important and challenging social and economic issues.

## Summary table

**31** Fill in the table.

| Strand of feminism | Key beliefs | Key thinkers |
|---|---|---|
| Liberal | | |
| Socialist | | |
| Radical | | |
| Black | | |
| Postmodern | | |

45

**32** In the context of feminism, what is meant by the term *reformist* and which strands of feminism could be described as reformist?    `2 marks`

..............................................................................................................................................

..............................................................................................................................................

**33** Outline THREE similarities in liberal, socialist and radical feminist thought.    `3 marks`

..............................................................................................................................................

..............................................................................................................................................

..............................................................................................................................................

**34** Outline THREE differences between liberal and socialist feminists.    `3 marks`

..............................................................................................................................................

..............................................................................................................................................

..............................................................................................................................................

**35** Outline THREE differences between liberal and radical feminists.    `3 marks`

..............................................................................................................................................

..............................................................................................................................................

..............................................................................................................................................

## Exam-style questions

**1** To what extent is equality rather than difference the goal of feminism? You must use appropriate thinkers you have studied to support your answer.    `35`  `24 marks`

*In the introduction, outline what is meant by both equality and difference. Why is the question being asked? Has this been a key division in feminist thought?*

..............................................................................................................................................

..............................................................................................................................................

..............................................................................................................................................

..............................................................................................................................................

..............................................................................................................................................

*Paragraph 1. Equality feminism is closely linked to liberal feminists, who aim for equality in the public sphere of politics, work and education. Thinkers: de Beauvoir, Gilman.*

..............................................................................................................................................

..............................................................................................................................................

..............................................................................................................................................

..............................................................................................................................................

*Paragraph 2. Equality feminism is closely linked to socialist feminism, but this is a view of equality that includes both class and gender. Thinker: Rowbotham.*

.....................................................................................................................................................................
.....................................................................................................................................................................
.....................................................................................................................................................................
.....................................................................................................................................................................
.....................................................................................................................................................................
.....................................................................................................................................................................
.....................................................................................................................................................................

*Paragraph 3. Equality feminism is linked to radical feminism, but this is a view of equality rooted in the private sphere of the family and interpersonal relations. Thinker: Millett.*

.....................................................................................................................................................................
.....................................................................................................................................................................
.....................................................................................................................................................................
.....................................................................................................................................................................
.....................................................................................................................................................................
.....................................................................................................................................................................
.....................................................................................................................................................................
.....................................................................................................................................................................

*Paragraph 4. Difference feminists dismiss equality as a limited, patriarchal and conservative aim.*

.....................................................................................................................................................................
.....................................................................................................................................................................
.....................................................................................................................................................................
.....................................................................................................................................................................
.....................................................................................................................................................................
.....................................................................................................................................................................
.....................................................................................................................................................................

*Conclusion. Is there a major division? Is difference feminism a minor or major movement? Is difference feminism even feminism?*

.....................................................................................................................................................................
.....................................................................................................................................................................
.....................................................................................................................................................................
.....................................................................................................................................................................
.....................................................................................................................................................................
.....................................................................................................................................................................

**2** **To what extent do feminists agree that 'the personal is political'? You must use appropriate thinkers you have studied to support your answer.**

35 · 24 marks

*Plan your answer below and write your essay on a separate sheet of paper.*

..........................................................................................
..........................................................................................
..........................................................................................
..........................................................................................
..........................................................................................
..........................................................................................
..........................................................................................
..........................................................................................
..........................................................................................
..........................................................................................
..........................................................................................
..........................................................................................

Hodder Education, an Hachette UK company, Blenheim Court, George Street, Banbury, Oxfordshire OX16 5BH

**Orders**

Bookpoint Ltd, 130 Park Drive, Milton Park, Abingdon, Oxfordshire OX14 4SB

tel: 01235 827720
fax: 01235 400401
e-mail: education@bookpoint.co.uk

Lines are open 9.00 a.m.–5.00 p.m., Monday to Saturday, with a 24-hour message answering service.

You can also order through the Hodder Education website: www.hoddereducation.co.uk

© Jessica Hardy and Clare Stansfield 2017

ISBN 978-1-4718-8960-8

First printed 2017

Impression number    5    4
Year                 2021  2020

This guide has been written specifically to support students preparing for the Edexcel A level Politics examinations. The content has been neither approved nor endorsed by Edexcel and remains the sole responsibility of the authors.

Typeset by Aptara, India

Printed in Dubai

Hachette UK's policy is to use papers that are natural, renewable and recyclable products and made from wood grown in sustainable forests. The logging and manufacturing processes are expected to conform to the environmental regulations of the country of origin.

ISBN 978-1-4718-8960-8

48